An
Irish Literary
Quiz Book

An Irish Literary Quiz Book

Paddy Lysaght

with illustrations by Tom Mathews

BRANDON

First published in Ireland 1984
Brandon Book Publishers Ltd
Dingle, Co. Kerry.

Cover design: Syd Bluett
Typesetting: Leaders Phototypesetting, Swords, Co. Dublin
Printed in Ireland by Cahill Printers Ltd, East Wall, Dublin 3.

To Sean and Liam

Introduction

THIS BOOK IS intended as a test, and a pretty strenuous one, of your knowledge of Irish literature, and especially of what is usually termed Anglo-Irish literature. It is something more than a quiz book in the usual sense; it is more like a Mastermind test. The written words of any particular author are what is important, and it is on them that this book is primarily based.

Besides giving you a fascinating glimpse into the range, diversity and richness found in our literature, this small book will, I hope, not only afford you amusement, but may also encourage you to read some of the authors mentioned and so add to your knowledge of some of these writers who have all contributed in their own ways to our literary heritage.

If you cannot find here a reference to your favourite Irish author, I would ask your forgiveness. There were simply too many to choose from. For instance, in the recently published *Dictionary of Irish Literature* edited by Robert Hogan, critical biographies – some short, some several pages long – are given for over 300 writers. I, as it were, only dipped my hand into this great store of richness, and plucked out this and that for your enjoyment.

QUESTIONS

Chapter 1

William Butler Yeats

1. What did he hear "in the deep heart's core"?

2. In the poem "Friends" he honoured three women who "have wrought what joy is in my days". Can you name these three?

3. How many swans did the poet see "Upon the brimming water among the stones" in the lake at Coole park?

4. To whom was he referring when he wrote: "I will have to hide him from our politicians, who are not yet ready for his doctrine"?

5. Where did the idea for "The Lake Isle of Innisfree" originate?

6. To whom was Yeats referring when he wrote: "I doubt if I should have done much with my life but for her firmness and her care"?

7. When the fiddler of Dooney played on his fiddle what did the people do?

8. With what did Aengus catch a little silver trout?

9. Why did wandering Aengus go out to the hazel wood?

10. Where did "the man who dreamed of faeryland" stand?

11. The following passage in a letter to an English friend records the poet's impressions of whom? "It was a curious experience, each recognised the other's point of view so completely. I had gone there full of suspicion, but my suspicion vanished at once."

12. According to Yeats, "From our birthday, until we die, It is but . . ."?

13. Late at night when a telephone message from the *Irish Times* and a telegram from the Swedish Ambassador came, telling him that he had won the Nobel Prize, what did Yeats and his wife do?

14. For how many summers was he the guest of Lady Gregory at Coole Park?

15. In what poem do the following lines used as Yeats's epitaph over his grave in Drumcliff, Co. Sligo occur?
    Cast a cold Eye
    On Life, on Death.
    Horseman, pass by!

16. Where and when did he die?

17. When was his body brought back to Ireland and re-interred at Drumcliff?

Answers on page 67

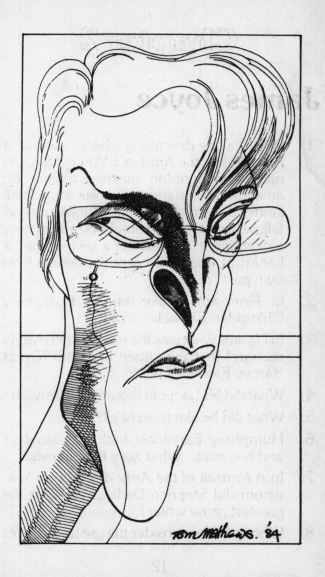

Chapter 2

James Joyce

1. Who was he describing when he wrote in *A Portrait of the Artist as a Young Man:* "A medical student, an oarsman, a tenor, an amateur actor, a shouting politician, a small landlord, a small investor, a drinker, a good fellow, a storyteller, somebody's secretary, something in a distillery, a taxgatherer, a bankrupt and at present a praiser of his own past"?

2. In *Finnegans Wake* who is Humphrey Chimpden Earwicker's wife?

3. In *Ulysses* what was the name of the mangy mongrel that the citizen had with him in Barney Kiernan's pub?

4. What did Mr Leopold Bloom eat with relish?

5. What did he like most of all?

6. Humphrey Earwicker had one daughter and two sons. What were their names?

7. In *A Portrait of the Artist as a Young Man* whom did Stephen Dedalus consider the greatest prose writer?

8. Whom did he consider the greatest poet?

9. Yeats wrote: "A little of it very beautiful and all of it very perfect technically." To which of Joyce's works was he referring?

10. In *A Portrait of the Artist as a Young Man* the extraordinary sermon on hell which scared young Stephen Dedalus out of his wits was given where and by whom?

11. Which one of Joyce's short stories might well have been named "Misses Morkan's Annual Dance"?

12. In which Dublin street was the committee room in the story "Ivy Day in the Committee Room"?

13. What song did Maria, the old lady who went to visit the Donnellys on Hallow Eve, sing?

14. Why did Father Dolan, the prefect of studies, slap Simon Dedalus on both hands?

15. Who went in the carriage with Bloom to Paddy Dignam's funeral?

16. After the funeral what did they do?

17. According to Ned Lambert when speaking to J. H. Menton, what did Bloom do for a living?

18. What was Molly Bloom's stage name?

19. Bloom, before he went to the National Library, decided to look for something to eat. What did he eventually eat and where?

20. In the evening Bloom stopped for a rest on the rocks of Sandymount strand. Can you name the three girls he saw there?

21. When Stephen Dedalus came home with Bloom to 7 Eccles Street at 2 a.m., what did they drink?

22. Bloom invited his guest to stay the night. Did he stay?

23. With what word does *Ulysses* end?

24. With what word does *Finnegans Wake* end?

Answers on page 69

what counterproposals were alter
nately advan   ed
accepted   ed,
modified,   ed,
declined,   re
stated   in
other te   re
accepted   ratified,
reconfo   ed ?
To   inaugurate
a pre-   arranged
course   of Italian
instruc   tion pla
ce th   e resid-
-ential   ence   of the.
instructed.

Tom Mathews. 1984.

Chapter 3

George Bernard Shaw and Oscar Wilde

1. Can you complete the following quotation "A man ought to be able to be fond of his wife without . . ."?

2. Everyone over forty is what according to Shaw?

3. To whom was Shaw referring when he wrote: "It would probably be a relief to me to dig him up and throw stones at him"?

4. Where is the locale of *Arms and the Man*?

5. Which of Shaw's plays opens with Adam and Eve in the Garden of Eden?

6. Shaw wrote, as he designated them himself, four pleasant plays, three unpleasant plays and three plays for puritans. Can you name them?

7. What did Mr Podgers, Lady Windermere's pet cheiromantist, tell poor Lady Fermor right out before everyone?

8. Who painted the fatal portrait of Dorian Gray and what eventually happened to him?

9. From whom did Lady Windermere get her fan?

10. Can you name the ideal husband in the play of that name?

11. Lady Windermere could resist everything except ... ?

12. What was Wilde's full name?

Answers on page 71

Chapter 4

Pen Names

The following were the pseudonyms of what authors?

1. Lynn Doyle.
2. Lord Dunsany.
3. Brinsley MacNamara.
4. Ethna Carbery.
5. John Eglinton.
6. The Bard of Thomond.
7. Father Prout.
8. Frank O'Connor.
9. Moira O'Neill.
10. *An Pilibín*.
11. George A. Birmingham.
12. *An Craoibhín Aoibhinn*.

Answers on page 73

Chapter 5

The following extracts are all from the works of well-known Irish writers; name the author of each.

1. The odd thing about you is that though you can write, you have all the credulities and illusions and innocence of the amateur and the collector. I won't have you write my life on any terms: Nellie would do it far better. You made Shakespeare a cross between a sailor in a melodrama and a French criminal invoking the memory of his sainted mother. What you would make of me not even God knows. You haven't the very faintest notion of the sort of animal I am.

2. When you kick out for yourself, Stephen — as I daresay you will one of these days — remember, whatever you do, to mix with gentlemen. When I was a young fellow I tell you I enjoyed myself. I mixed with fine decent fellows. Everyone of us could do something. One fellow had a good voice, another fellow was a good actor, another could sing a good comic song, another was a good oarsman or a good racket player,

another could tell a good story and so on. We kept the ball rolling anyhow and enjoyed ourselves and saw a bit of life and we were none the worse for it either. But we were all gentlemen, Stephen – at least I hope we were – and bloody good honest Irishmen too.

3. One day I was walking over a bit of marshy ground close to Inchy Wood when I felt, all of a sudden, and only for a second, an emotion which I said to myself was the root of Christian mysticism. There had swept over me a sense of weakness, of dependence on a great personal Being somewhere far off yet near at hand. No thought of mine had prepared me for this emotion, for I had been pre-occupied with Aengus and Edain, and with Manannan, son of the sea.

4. All aspects of my native country are violently disagreeable to me, and I cannot think of the place I was born in without a sensation akin to nausea.

5. I do not wish to write a book of wonders but rather to bring thought back to the Being whom the ancient seers worshipped as Deity. I believe that most of what was said of God was in reality said of that Spirit whose body is Earth. I must in some fashion indicate the nature of the visions which led me to believe with Plato that the earth is

not at all what the geographers suppose it to be, and that we live like frogs at the bottom of a marsh knowing nothing of that Many-Coloured Earth which is superior to this we know, yet related to it as soul to body. On that Many-Coloured Earth, he tells us, live a divine folk, and there are temples wherein the gods do truly dwell, and I wish to convey, so far as words may, how some apparitions of that ancient beauty came to me in wood or on hillside or by the shores of the western sea.

6. It is related in the **Annals** that for the first four centuries after its foundation by the blessed Kieran the monastic settlement of Clonmacnoise enjoyed a singular immunity from the visitation of imps and ghouls, night fiends, goblins and all sorts of hellish phantoms which not unseldom appear to men.

7. He would leave Yeats on his Island of Innisfree, standing pensively at the door of his small cabin of clay and wattles made; or moving, slow and moody, between his nine bean rows, thinking of peace where there was no peace; for Ireland's red-rose-bordered hem was muddy now, and ragged. There was no making love to Cathleen, daughter of Houlihan, now, untidy termagant, bawling out her prayers. He would leave Lady Gregory watching

wild swans rising from the lake, or walking in her Seven Woods of Coole.

8. This old man talks usually in a mournful tone about his ill health, and his death which he feels to be approaching, yet he has occasional touches of humour that remind me of old Mourteen on the north island. To-day a grotesque twopenny doll was lying on the floor near the old woman. He picked it up and examined it as if comparing it with her. Then he held it up: "Is it you is after bringing that thing into the world," he said, "woman of the house?"

9. The Research Bureau is facing up to the problem posed by the jam shortage. The proposal to generate jam from second-hand electricity is being thoroughly investigated and a spokesman prominent in industrial jams — perhaps too prominent — revealed last night that experiments show that the inquiry "will not be fruitless".

10. "Young people," said the Philosopher, "do not know what age is, and old people forget what youth was. When you begin to grow old always think deeply of your youth, for an old man without memories is a wasted life, and nothing is worth remembering but our childhood ... "

11. Being Mr Shaw's secretary was only a form of words. I had no duties, I never as much

as typed a letter for him, but as his "secretary" I could attend all his rehearsals, a privilege which Mr Granville-Barker and Dion Boucicault also extended to me. Yeats had rooms in London in which I stayed, everything was made as easy for me as possible.

12. My mother's maiden name was Bridget Murphy. She was born in 1865 on a twenty-five acre farm called Loughill on the banks of the little River Deel, two or three miles from the town of Rathkeale, deep in the flat, flat lands of West Limerick. She was very tall, slim as a reed and quite beautiful, with liquid sapphire eyes shadowed by an inborn melancholy.

13. Our Galway rooms were on Nun's Island on the outskirts of the city, where the silence, the low stone bridges, and the gaunt houses dipping their walls into the canals, gave a disconsolate and ghostly illusion of Venice, the pearl and marble palaces giving way to grey warehouses. Here we ate and smoked and talked, and played Borodin and de Falla on the gramophone, and here too we made all the designs and projects for the opening production of the new Gaelic Theatre.

Answers on page 74

Chapter 6

1. One of Maurice Walsh's best known novels is sub-titled, "Being the chronicles of the Wars of Montrose as seen by Martin Somers, Adjutant of women in O'Cahan's Regiment". What is the title of this novel?

2. Who, according to Myles na gCopaleen:
   Made good recensions
   Of ancient declensions,
   And careful redactions
   To their three satisfactions.

3. What are the names of the country girls in Edna O'Brien's novel of that title?

4. Who wrote, "It would be a noble achievement to abolish the Irish language in the Kingdom"?

5. In *The Spacious Adventures of the Man in the Street,* by Eimar O'Duffy, the clerk O'Kennedy found that the people of Bulnid practiced monophagy. What is monophagy?

6. Lord Byron wrote, "I have heard that man speak more poetry than I have ever seen written, though I saw him seldom". Whom had he in mind?

7. *Tales of the O'Hara Family* were written by two Kilkenny brothers. What were their names?

8. To what work of Thomas Moore was Mr Luttrell referring when he wrote:
   > I'm told, dear Moore, your lays are sung
   > (Can it be true, you lucky man?)
   > By moonlight, in the Persian tongue,
   > Along the streets of Ispahan.

9. Who had just died when Daniel O'Connell wrote this note to his National Association? "As I stand alone in the solitude of my mountains, many a tear shall I shed in memory of the noble youth. Oh! how vain are words or tears when such a national calamity afflicts the country ..."

10. Hugh Forbes or Aodh MacFirbis is a well-known Maurice Walsh character. By what name is he better known?

11. In Flann O'Brien's *At Swim-Two-Birds* to whom was the Pooka MacPhillimey married?

12. Which of Goldsmith's characters was "passing rich with £40 a year"?

Answers on page 76

Chapter 7

1. John Keegan, a poet born in 1809 in Queen's County, wrote a ballad the first four lines of which run:

   > One Winter's day, long, long ago,
   > When I was a little fellow,
   > A piper wandered to our door,
   > Grey-headed, blind and yellow.

   What was the name of the piper?

2. Who had George Russell (AE) in mind when he wrote:

   > Here's to you, men I never met,
   > But hope to meet behind the veil,
   > Thronged on same starry parapet
   > That looks down upon Innisfail.

3. In Peadar O'Donnell's novel *Islanders*, what did Mary Manus do immediately after Mary Doogan's death?

4. Conor Cruise O'Brien's first book, *Maria Cross*, written under the pseudonym Donat O'Donnell, is a study of eight writers who are Roman Catholics. Can you name these writers?

5. Who is the central figure in Sean O'Faolain's novel *A Nest of Simple Folk*?

6. A novel in the form of a biography of one Bernard Vandaleur, in which such well-known personalities as Mr de Valera, Jack B. Yeats, Oliver St John Gogarty, James Dillon and many others pass through the story, was published in 1959. What is the title of the novel and who wrote it?

7. Benedict Kiely wrote a critical biography entitled *Poor Scholar* of what Irish writer?

8. *Shadow and Substance,* reputedly Paul Vincent Carroll's finest play, focuses on a conflict between a canon and a school-master. What were their names?

9. What Irish writer received the Croix de Guerre for his activities in the French Resistance during World War II?

10. In *Innisfallen Fare Thee Well,* Sean O'Casey described a well-known Irish personality thus: "She looked like an old elegant nun of a new order, a blend of the Lord Jesus Christ and of Puck, an order that Ireland had never known before, and wasn't likely to know again for a long time to come." Whom was he describing?

11. Who, according to Patrick Kavanagh, killed James Joyce?

12. In Frank O'Connor's famous story "Guests of the Nation" what were the names of the two English hostages who were eventually

shot in reprisal for four Irishmen who were shot in Cork?

Answers on page 77

Chapter 8

1. John Ruskin said of an Irish author that, "He could have written all my books about landscape and pictures." Whom had he in mind?

2. Which Irish novel published in 1971 won the *Guardian* Fiction Prize, the Royal Irish Academy of Letters – Allied Banks Prize and the Royal Society for Literature Heinemann Award?

3. In what is probably his best known poem, Francis Ledwidge wrote:
   He shall not hear the bittern cry
   In the wild sky where he is lain,
   Nor voices of the sweeter birds
   Above the wailing of the rain.
   To whom was he referring?

4. Where did Pádraic Ó Conaire buy his little black ass?

5. In the poem "Shancoduff", Patrick Kavanagh says: "My black hills have never seen the sun rising". Why?

6. Who said this to Dr Johnson? "If you were to make little fishes talk, they would talk like whales."

7. What Irishman said that a king may make a nobleman but he cannot make a gentleman.

8. Who wrote these lines?
   Their knickers are made of
      crêpe-de-Chine,
   Their shoes are made of python,
   Their halls are lined with tiger rugs,
   And their walls with heads of bison.

9. Can you name the two women the two philosophers married in James Stephens' *The Crock of Gold*?

10. Besides a boy (unnamed) there are only four other characters in Beckett's *Waiting for Godot*. Can you name them?

11. What Irish author, on moving to Dublin from London, scandalised his neighbourhood by painting his front door Fenian green?

12. Add the next two lines to Patrick Kavanagh's poem "A Christmas Childhood".
    My father played the melodeon,
    My mother milked the cows,

Answers on page 78

Tom Merkens.

Chapter 9

1. Who said that men come of age at sixty, women at fifteen?

2. *Performing Flea* is the title of P. G. Wodehouse's autobiography. Where did he get this title?

3. Who wrote, "When I die I want to decompose in a barrel of porter and have it served in all the pubs in Dublin"?

4. In *The Hostage*, Brendan Behan gives a humorous definition of an Anglo-Irishman. It is?

5. *The Various Lives of Marcus Igoe* is reputedly one of Brinsley MacNamara's best novels. What trade did Marcus follow?

6. What was his wife's name?

7. In what O'Casey play will you find the famous line, "The whole world is in a state of chassis"?

8. For whom did the boy in *Waiting for Godot* work?

9. Frances Browne wrote a book called *Granny's Wonderful Chair* which was very widely read in the last quarter of the last century. What was the book about?

10. When the play *General John Regan* was presented in Westport, Co. Mayo in 1914, it occasioned a night of rioting possibly more violent than the *Playboy* riots at the Abbey Theatre. Who wrote this play?

11. To whom was Yeats referring when he wrote, "He is all blood, dirt and sucked sugar stick"?

12. What Irishman was appointed Poet Laureate of England in 1692?

Answers on page 79

Chapter 10

1. J. M. Synge said that he got more aid than any learning would have given him from a chink in the floor of the old house where he was staying, that let him hear what was being said by the servant girls in the kitchen. What play was he writing at this time?

2. Who wrote this?
   So naturalists observe a flea
   Hath smaller fleas that on him prey;
   And these have smaller fleas to bite 'em,
   And so proceed ad infinitum.

3. Louis D'Alton's play *The Man in the Cloak*, staged in the Abbey in 1937, is based on the life of what well-known Irish poet?

4. In *Castle Rackrent*, Maria Edgeworth's tale of the family of that name over three generations is told by the family steward. What was his name?

5. Who said that "Ireland is an old sow that eats her farrow"?

6. In 1893 Padraig O'Brien, at 46 Cuffe Street, Dublin, published an edition of a poem in Irish which he entitled *Mediae Noctis Consilium*. What is its title in English?

7. What is the title of the well-known novel in which the wheat king buys up all the wild birds in the world and cages them to satisfy a whim of his queen?

8. Why did Patrick O'Kelly, an 18th century poet, curse Doneraile?

9. Who said: "I don't believe in publishers who wish to butter their bannocks on both sides while they'll hardly allow an author to smell treacle"?

10. To what bird was Gerald Griffin referring when he wrote:

    White bird of the tempest! Oh, beautiful thing,

    With the bosom of snow, and the motionless wing.

11. Who, according to Thomas Davis, is "as fair as Shannon's side and purer than its water"?

12. A collection of short stories by an Irish author has a central character Belacqua Shuah moving through them. Name the book and the author.

Answers on page 80

Chapter 11

1. Which very well-known Irish novel is sub-titled "A Story gathered from the Stray Leaves of an Old Diary"?

2. Extraordinary as it may seem, Jules Verne wrote a book about Ireland. What is its title?

3. When Rose Kavanagh died in 1891 at the youthful age of 32, W. B. Yeats described her as "a noble, merry and gentle personality". She was a gifted young poet whose poetry is unfortunately now forgotten. But apart from her poetic gift there is another reason why she might be remembered by some. Why?

4. Who had Benedict Kiely in mind when he wrote: "It is hard to know how to meet the illogicality of a man who writes well in English about Ireland and is then, apparently, prepared to maintain that only writing in Irish can properly express the soul of the Irish people"?

5. "As a matter of historical fact I know that I was born in 1903 when we were living in Douglas Street, Cork, over a small sweet-

and-tobacco shop kept by a middle-aged lady called Wall." This is the first sentence of whose autobiography?

6. Lionel Johnson wrote of an Irish poet: "He is the poet of much else that is imperishable; but above all he is the poet of a poem foremost among the world's poems of inspired patriotism." What poet was he referring to and which poem?

7. An Irish writer, now unfortunately neglected, was considered by Yeats, AE and several others to have initiated the Irish Literary Revival. He has been called "The father of the Irish Renaissance." Who was he?

8. Frank Gallagher, historian, journalist, editor and one time director of Radio Éireann, wrote a book entitled *Four Glorious Years*. What is the work about?

9. Who wrote this? "Praise be to God! I little thought at one time in my life that such an important piece of literary work lay hidden in my mother's old grey head."

10. In *The Big Chapel*, Thomas Kilroy's novel based on anticlerical riots in Co. Kilkenny in the 1870s, what was the name of the parish priest who was suspended by his bishop?

11. Where did Fr Edward Letheby, the new curate in Canon Sheehan's novel, serve

before coming to Fr Dan at Kilronan?

12. It is not generally known that one of the most successful thriller writers in the English language was born in County Clare. Who?

Answers on page 81

Chapter 12

1. "I'm an old woman now, with one foot in the grave and the other on its edge. I have experienced much ease and much hardship from the day I was born until this very day." These are the first two sentences of whose autobiography?

2. To whom was George Moore referring when he wrote, "You're always right ... what an inveterate mystic you are, as practical as St Teresa ... You are a cleverer man than I ... "?

3. What river is Francis MacManus referring to in his novel *Flow on, Lovely River*?

4. Can you name the trilogy of novels Francis MacManus wrote based on peasant life in 18th century Ireland?

5. Who is the central character of these three novels?

6. Who is the hero of Standish O'Grady's novel *The Flight of the Eagle*?

7. In *The Dalkey Archive* by Flann O'Brien, what is the name of the barman who writes pamphlets for the Catholic Truth Society?

8. A County Down woman has the unenviable distinction of writing what have been called the worst novels ever published. Her name and the titles of her three novels?

9. In 1914 Patrick MacGill wrote a novel about the Irish migrant labourers in Scotland, which became very popular and which was recently republished. What is the title of this novel?

10. What does Walter Macken's novel *The Scorching Wind* deal with?

11. Name two Irish writers considered among the best ghost story writers in the English language.

12. The plot of a well-known Irish novel might vaguely be summarised thus: A nameless narrator is writing a book about another writer called Dermot Trellis who is also writing a book. The characters in Trellis's book are so anxious to be left alone by their creator that they try to keep him asleep as much as possible. But Trellis manages to create a female character, Sheila Lamont, with whom he falls in love – and so on and so forth. What is the name of the book and who is the author?

Answers on page 82

Chapter 13

1. The following sentences occur in the first paragraph of what well-known Irish autobiography? "I am the scrapings of the pot, the last of the litter. That's why I was left so long at the breasts. I was a spoiled child, too."

2. In October 1952, *The Leader,* now defunct but then a well-known Dublin weekly paper, published a "Profile" of a poet predicting that he "will be gratefully remembered by the Irish nation for what is probably the best poem written in Ireland since Goldsmith gave us 'The Deserted Village'." The poem and its author?

3. Where did Brian O'Nolan get his pseudonym Myles na gCopaleen?

4. Who wrote this letter, in 1812, of which the following is only an extract? It describes an extraordinary attempt by an Englishman, who afterwards became famous, to restore Ireland's Parliament and bring about Catholic Emancipation. "I have already sent 400 of my Irish pamphlets into the world and they have excited a sensation of

wonder in Dublin . . . I stand at the balcony of our window and watch till I see a man who looks likely and I throw a book at him."

5. Who said this about John Mitchel? "Poor Mitchel, I told him he would most likely be hanged, but I told him too, that they could not hang the immortal part of him."

6. Who do you think wrote the following? "Oliver Goldsmith flourished in the eighteenth and nineteenth centuries. He lived to be a hundred and three years old, and in that age may justly be styled the sun of literature and the Confucius of Europe."

7. Can you name the author and the title of a first novel which had a very enthusiastic preface by Sean O'Faolain who claimed that "if she does not follow up this first book with a set of novels about the crowded world of her childhood she is simply throwing away a store of wealth that any writer will envy from the bottom of his heart." The novel has also a most unusual dedication, reading thus: "To Trush, my brother, who has always been the buttermilk for my soda-bread."

8. "The many indications he has given of a liberal mind in the expenditure of money has left a vacuum in my purse, as well as an

impression on my mind, not easily erad-
icated." This is an extract from a letter
from one brother, giving his opinion about
his nephew to that nephew's father. The
nephew subsequently became very
famous. Who was he?

9. Give the next two lines after:
   She lived beside the Anner
   At the foot of Slievenamon."

10. What is the title of that poem and who
   wrote it?

11. Why is Leon Uris's massive novel about
   Northern Ireland between the end of the
   19th century and the 1916 Rising entitled
   Trinity.

12. What is Conor Cruise O'Brien's play
   Murderous Angels about?

Answers on page 83

Chapter 14

1. Freeman Wills Crofts, the son of a British army officer, was born in Dublin in 1879. Besides radio plays and short stories he wrote several detective stories featuring a police inspector. What was the name of this inspector?

2. William Pembroke Mulchinock, the son of a wealthy merchant, is scarcely remembered today, yet he wrote the words of one of the best-known Irish songs. What is the name of this song?

3. Thomas Paine wrote *The Rights of Man* in reply to an equally well-known book published by an Irishman in 1790. Can you name this book and its author?

4. John Burke, whose *Genealogical and Heraldic History of the Peerage, Baronetage and Knightage of the United Kingdom* (1826) has been described as "a stud book of humanity, unmatched in Western Europe", was an Irishman. Where and when was he born?

5. Can you name the economist, born in north Kerry in 1680, who has been called the "father of political economy" because of

his one famous book, *Essai sur la nature du commerce en general,* published in 1755?

6. Pádraig Ó Siochfhradha (1883-1964), author, teacher, Gaelic League organiser, editor and director, is better known by his pen name and for the two ever popular books which he wrote. What was his pen name and the titles of the two books?

7. An Irish doctor, while imprisoned in a Japanese internment camp in Borneo during World War II, wrote a novel which was published in Dublin in 1946. Can you name the author and the novel?

8. What were the Christian names of *Hanrahan's Daughter* in Patrick Purcell's novel of that title?

9. This book was praised by Sir Walter Scott and translated into German by the brothers Grimm. Its author was born in Cork in 1798. He helped to found the Camden Society, the Percy Society and the British Archaeological Association. He was also a Fellow of the Society of Antiquaries and of many continental societies. Can you name him and his book?

10. Gerald Griffin's poem on the seagull is, after his tender lyric "Aileen Aroon", possibly his best-known poem. Can you give the full title of this poem?

11. In *The Straight and Narrow Path*, Honor Tracy's amusing but astringent novel about Irish country life, the nuns of the Convent of the Immaculate Conception in Patrickstown were on Mid-Summer's Eve celebrating the day in a manner as inappropriate as it was charming. How were they celebrating?

12. What was the *Kottabos*?

Answers on page 85

Chapter 15

Each of the following is the first sentence or two of a novel of Irish interest. Most of these extracts give some clue which should help you place them; how many of the novels can you identify?

1. The young women of Cloone had not come to see the hares die: rather they had come to see the young men live.

   Swaggering, Finn Dillon and I left the frosty sunlight and entered the marquee.

2. This apparent account of about two years of his life was found among the late Patrick Riley's socks, rags and papers after his death.

3. My soul, so far as I understand it, has very kindly taken colour and form from the many various modes of life that self-will and an impetuous temperament have forced me to indulge in. Therefore I may say that I am free from original qualities, defects, tastes, etc.

4. Have ever you visited that portion of Erin's plot that offers its sympathetic soil for the

minute survey and scrutinous examination of those in political power, whose decision has wisely been the means before now of converting the stern and prejudiced, and reaching the hand of slight aid to share its strength in augmenting its agricultural richness? If you have not already reached the western borders of your native and beloved isle of green and striking grandeur, you are hardly worthy of permission to dawdle in your existence or dwindle your lives of dull monotony into hoped-for futurity.

5. His window looked onto a derelict mill half-hidden by a small wood above the three ponds, each on a slightly lower level.

6. It was shortly before noon of a day in March 1879, at the village of Manister on the coast of County Mayo. Elizabeth Henry St George was sitting at her desk in a corner of the living-room at Manister Lodge, drawing up the household weekly accounts.

7. Mary Makebelieve lived with her mother in a small room at the very top of a big, dingy house in a Dublin back street.

8. I, Thomas King of Loch Ruighi, will begin this narrative with a relation of the events that befell me – and my friends – on a July day in the Province of Moray.

9. Ana did not wait for the king in the porch of her house. She stood above it, in her drawing-room, on the threshold of the central, balconied window. From there she could overlook the market-place, which was outside the open forecourt of her house, and she was spared the courtier-fuss of her son, Rodrigo.

10. Mary Kate's mother was going away to Dublin. For weeks this had been dinned into the child's mind by all her acquaintances, normal and grown-up.

11. Keys were rattled, heavy bolts drawn and the iron-bound gates of Clonmel gaol swung open.

12. Big Magee wasn't on the train. His red face wasn't among the faces that came bobbing up the long smoky platform.

Answers on page 86

Chapter 16

1. What was the name of the murderer who killed the secretary of the local branch of the Farmers' Union during the farm-labourers' strike in Liam O'Flaherty's novel *The Informer*?

2. What was the name of the informer in O'Flaherty's novel?

3. Who wrote this about a well-known Dublin building?
   A "dull stone set in the ring of the city's ignorance."

4. What novelist married a famous beauty, bred racehorses, owned a poultry farm and was imprisoned at the time of the Irish Civil War, and although he was born in Queensland, Australia, is now generally regarded as an Irish novelist?

5. According to William Allingham,
   Down along the rocky shore,
   Some make their home;
   They live on crispy pancakes
   Of yellow tide-foam.
   Who are these strange people?

6. Do you know the title of Sir Samuel Ferguson's well-known poem which begins:
   > I walked through Ballinderry in the springtime,
   > When the bud was on the tree?

7. To whom was John Mitchel referring when he wrote: "For those who were not close witnesses of Irish politics in that day – who did not see how vast this giant figure loomed in Ireland and in England for a generation and a half – it is not easy to understand the strong emotion caused by his death both in friends and enemies"?

8. Ethel Mannin's *Two Studies in Integrity* is a study in opposites of two Irishmen. Who were these two?

9. Lady Dufferin wrote a satire, now forgotten, on high life in the nineteenth century called *The Honourable Impulsia Gushington*, but she also wrote a ballad, a universal favourite. Do you know the name of this ballad?

10. The *Times Literary Supplement* described a present day Irish poet as "Keyed and pitched unlike any other significant poet at work in the language anywhere." What Irish poet was it discussing?

11. The most celebrated case of book-banning in Ireland was undoubtedly the banning "for being in its general tendency

indecent". of Eric Cross's *The Tailor and Ansty*.

It was debated for four days in the Senate, and the quotations from the book read out at the debate were ordered to be struck from the record. What was the tailor's name?

12. Margaret Barrington, who married Liam O'Flaherty in 1926 and separated from him in 1932, wrote one novel. Can you name it?

Answers on page 87

Chapter 17

Do you know the authors of the following quotations?

1. "Not very well, I can only write prose today."

2. "Martyrdom is the only way in which a man can become famous without ability."

3. "It (Dublin) is a city where you can see a sparrow fall to the ground and God watching it."

4. "A face on him as long as a late breakfast."

5. "To marry the Irish is to look for poverty."

6. "I am signing my death warrant."

7. "We are all born mad. Some remain so."

8. "Superstition is the religion of feeble minds."

9. "Man wants but little here below, nor wants that little long."

10. "A man cannot be too careful in the choice of his enemies."

11. "We are fond of one another, because our ailments are the same."

12. "She's as headstrong as an allegory on the banks of the Nile."

Answers on page 88

Chapter 18

Each of the following twelve extracts is the beginning of a short story by a well-known Irish writer. All of the authors are justly famous; most of them figure in at least one anthology of Irish short stories. Can you give the title of each extract and name its author?

1. Patrick Feeney's cabin was crowded with people. In the large kitchen men, women, and children lined the walls, three deep in places, sitting on forms, chairs, stools, and on one another's knees.

2. "They might wear whites," she had said, as she stood sipping her tea and looking down at the suburban tennis players in the square. And then, turning her head in that swift movement that always reminded him of a jackdaw: "By the way, Bobby, will you drive me up to Lough Derg next week?"

3. Ivor O'Donovan knew that it was Ted Driscoll had called him: raising himself above the edge of the bunk he was just in time to see him manoeuvering that bear-like body of his through the narrow little hatchway, to see the splintery shutter slap to behind him.

4. Lily, the caretaker's daughter, was literally run off her feet. Hardly had she brought one gentleman into the little pantry behind the office on the ground floor and helped him off with his overcoat, than the wheezy hall-door bell clanged again and she had to scamper along the bare hallway to let in another guest.

5. Everything was ready, the suitcase closed, her black velvet coat-collar carefully brushed, and a list pinned to the wall reminding her husband when to feed the hens and turkeys, and what foodstuffs to give them.

6. For weeks it was nothing but simony and sacrilege, and the sins crying to heaven for vengeance, the big green Catechism in our hands, walking home along the North Circular Road.

7. The upper landing of our house had brown linoleum on it and outside each of the bedroom doors there was a small black mat.

8. One day, in my first job, a lady fell in love with me. It was quite unreasonable, of course, for I wasn't wonderful: I was small and thin, and I weighed much the same as a largish duck-egg.

9. They cut the tongues of the dead foxes brought to the barracks and threw them to

the grey cat or across the netting wire into the garden. They cut the tongues out of the foxes so that the same fox couldn't be brought back again for the half-crown the government gave for each dead fox in its campaign for the extermination of foxes.

10. "That dunghill isn't doing anybody any harm and it's not going out of where it is as long as I'm in this house!" said Phelim Molloy.

11. Father was in the army all through the war — the first war, I mean — so, up to the age of five, I never saw much of him, and what I saw did not worry me.

12. Jacky Cardew is one of those club bachelors who are so well groomed, well preserved, pomaded, medicated, and self-cosseted that they seem ageless – the sort of fixture about whom his pals will say when he comes unstuck around the age of eighty, "Well, well! Didn't poor old Jacky Cardew go off very fast in the end?"

Answers on page 89

Chapter 19

1. What was the name of the major who took up residence at Shreelane as the Resident Magistrate in Somerville and Ross's *Some Experiences of an Irish R.M.*?

2. What was the relationship between E.Œ. Somerville and Martin Ross?

3. In 1940 Austin Clarke and Robert Farren founded a society in Dublin to produce verse plays for radio. What was this society called?

4. A play published in 1961 could be summarised as being about tinkers trying to reach a hospital before their baby is born. Its title and author?

5. Which one of Walter Macken's novels deals with the Cromwellian plantation in the 17th century?

6. What is the title of the play by Brian Friel, published in 1964, which deals with the problem of Gareth O'Donnell who has decided rather reluctantly to emigrate to America?

7. What is the theme of James Plunkett's novel *Strumpet City*?

8. Anthony Trollope recalls in his autobiography that one day in 1843 while walking with his friend and guest John Merivale in County Leitrim, they came upon a melancholy ruin of a country house. While still among the ruins of this house, he says that the idea of the plot of his first novel came to him. What is the title of this his first novel, which has a purely Irish theme?

9. What is the setting for Brian Moore's novel, *Catholics*, published in 1972?

10. An entertaining crime story was serialised by the *Irish Times* in 1953 and published in book form as *The Scraperer* in 1964. Who wrote it?

11. A large estate in rural Ireland is the setting for John Banville's second novel, *Birchwood*. Can you name the family to which this estate belonged?

12. "The Little Black Rose" and "The Silk of the Kine" are two phrases used by Aubrey de Vere in the one poem by which he is now remembered, *"The Little Black Rose."* What does he mean by both phrases?

Answers on page 90

Chapter 20

1. In *Glenanaar*, Canon Sheehan's famous story, the Yank, throwing away a half-burned cigar and calmly divesting himself of coat and waistcoat, went in as a substitute for the local captain who had been taken ill, and to everybody's surprise and delight, cut his way upfield and scored the winning goal. What was the Yank's name?

2. For years Aodh de Blacam wrote a very widely read article almost daily in the *Irish Press*, using the pen name Rody the Rover. Where did he get this pen name?

3. Piaris Béaslaí, Frank O'Connor and Rex Taylor: what have they in common?

4. In *Ulysses*, Joyce featured three young men in the Martello tower in Sandycove named Buck Mulligan, Haines and Stephen Dedalus. Stephen Dedalus is Joyce himself. Who were the other two?

5. Douglas Hyde is credited with writing the first play in Irish that was produced at a professional theatre (the Gaiety Theatre in 1901). What is the name of the play?

6. What Irish author secured a post (which he held only for a few months) as Registrar of the Admiralty Prize Court in Bermuda in 1804?

7. Who wrote this about George Moore: "George is a pleasant fellow to meet, and if I read the book *Hail and Farewell* I might not be able to meet him again"?

8. The following note was found beside the bed where this playwright died: "Author is prepared to sell outright all rights in 14 plays dealing intimately with life in the Irish countryside. Most have already been either printed or published." Who was he?

9. Do you know the author and the title of a play written in 1904 in which one deaf Mrs Tarpey, an apple-seller from the village of Cloon, creates a crazy disturbance through her talk?

10. Dr Oliver St John Gogarty took exception to a sentence in a book as he considered that it cast aspersions on his wife. It was the subject of a libel action which Gogarty won. Can you name the book, the author, and possibly give the sentence Gogarty objected to?

11. A professor, happily still with us, was to have written the authorised biography of W. B. Yeats, but he withdrew when he

found that other scholars had access to Yeats's unpublished material. Who is this professor?

12. What Dublin theatre was founded by Hilton Edwards and Micheal MacLiammóir?

Answers on page 91

Answers

Chapter 1

William Butler Yeats

1. " . . . Lake water lapping with low sounds by the shore". ("The Lake Isle of Innisfree")

2. Lady Gregory, Maude Gonne and Olivia Shakespeare.

3. "Nine-and-fifty swans". ("The Wild Swans at Coole")

4. James Joyce. Yeats was reading *Ulysses* at the time.

5. "When walking through Fleet Street very homesick I heard a little tinkle of water and saw a fountain in a shop window which balanced a little ball upon its jet, and began to remember lake water. From the sudden remembrance came my poem 'Innisfree'. "

6. Lady Augustus Gregory.

7. They danced "like a wave of the sea". ("The Fiddler of Dooney")

8. With a berry hooked to a thread. ("The Song of Wandering Aengus")

9. "Because a fire was in my head." ("The Song of Wandering Aengus")

10. " ... among a crowd at Drumahair". ("The Man Who Dreamed of Faeryland")

11. Eamon de Valera.

12. " ... the winking of an eye." ("To Ireland in the Coming Times")

13. "At half past twelve my wife and I are alone, and search the cellar for a bottle of wine, but it is empty, and as a celebration is necessary we cook sausages."

14. For twenty summers, from 1897 until he rebuilt his tower at Ballylee.

15. "Under Ben Bulben."

16. At Roquebrune, on Saturday, 28 January 1939.

17. On 17 September 1948.

Chapter 2

James Joyce

1. His father, John Stanislaus Joyce.
2. Anna Livia Plurabelle.
3. Garryowen.
4. " . . . the inner organs of beasts and fowls."
5. " . . . grilled mutton kidneys which gave to his palate a fine tang of faintly scented urine."
6. Isabel, Shem and Shaun.
7. Cardinal Newman.
8. Lord Byron.
9. *Chamber Music*.
10. In Clongowes Wood College, at a table on the left of the altar, by one Father Arnall.
11. "The Dead". The story is based on what happened at this dance.
12. Wicklow Street.
13. "I Dreamt I Dwelt in Marble Halls".

14. Because, although Stephen had broken his glasses and was exempted from writing like the others, the prefect of studies would not accept this explanation.

15. Martin Cunningham, Simon Dedalus and Mr Power.

16. Paid a short visit of respect to Parnell's grave.

17. He was a traveller for blotting paper and also a canvasser for advertisements.

18. Madame Marion Tweedy.

19. He had a cheese sandwich and a glass of burgundy in Davy Byrne's pub at 21 Duke Street.

20. Cissy Caffrey, Edy Boardman and Gerty MacDowell.

21. A teacup of Epp's soluble cocoa.

22. No; when the church bells rang out, he went away.

23. Yes.

24. The.

Chapter 3

George Bernard Shaw and Oscar Wilde

1. " . . . making a fool of himself about her."
2. A scoundrel.
3. William Shakespeare.
4. Bulgaria during the war with Serbia in 1885.
5. *Back to Methuselah.*
6. The four pleasant plays are *Arms and the Man, Candida, The Man of Destiny* and *You Never Can Tell.* The three unpleasant plays are *Widowers' Houses, The Philanderer* and *Mrs Warren's Profession.* The three plays for puritans are *The Devil's Disciple, Caesar and Cleopatra* and *Captain Brassbound's Conversion.*
7. That she did not care a bit for music but was extremely fond of musicians.
8. Basil Hallward who in the end was stabbed to death by Dorian Gray.

9. From her husband. It was his birthday present to her on her coming of age.

10. Sir Robert Chiltern.

11. Temptation.

12. Oscar Fingal O'Flahertie Wills Wilde.

Chapter 4

Pen Names

1. Leslie Alexander Montgomery.
2. Edward John Morton Drax Plunkett.
3. John Weldon.
4. Anna Johnston MacManus.
5. William Kirkpatrick Magee.
6. Michael Hogan.
7. Rev. Francis Sylvester Mahony.
8. Michael O' Donovan.
9. Agnes Nesta Higginson.
10. John Hackett Pollock.
11. Canon James Owen Hannay.
12. Dr Douglas Hyde.

Chapter 5

Who Wrote This?

1. Extract from a letter from George Bernard Shaw to Frank Harris who had proposed to write a biography of Shaw.

2. James Joyce in *A Portrait of the Artist as a Young Man*, purporting to be the advice given to young Stephen Dedalus by his father.

3. William Butler Yeats in *The Celtic Twilight*.

4. George Moore in *Confessions of a Young Man*.

5. George Russell (AE) in *The Candle of Vision*.

6. Mervyn Wall in *The Unfortunate Fursey*.

7. Sean O'Casey in *Inishfallen Fare Thee Well*.

8. John M. Synge in *The Aran Islands*.

9. Myles na gCopaleen in his "Cruiskeen Lawn" column in *The Irish Times*.

10. James Stephens in *The Crock of Gold*.

11. Lennox Robinson in his autobiography *Curtain Up*.

12. Sean O'Faolain in his autobiography *Vive Moi*.

13. Michael MacLiammóir's *All for Hecuba*.

Chapter 6

1. *And No Quarter*.
2. Binchy and Bergin and Best.
3. Caithleen Brady and Baba Brennan.
4. Jonathan Swift.
5. Choosing a single food and continuing to eat it all one's life.
6. John Philpot Curran.
7. John and Michael Banim.
8. His long poem, *Lalla Rookh*.
9. Thomas Osborne Davis in 1845 in his thirty-first year.
10. The Small Dark Man.
11. One of the Corrigans of Carlow.
12. The village Preacher in *The Deserted Village*.

Chapter 7

1. Caoch O'Leary.
2. Those who took part in the 1916 rebellion.
3. Mary Manus closed her lips, and put a prayer book under her chin to keep the mouth shut, and then they all cried.
4. François Mauriac, Georges Bernanos, Graham Greene, Sean O'Faolain, Evelyn Waugh, Leon Bloy, Paul Claudel and Charles Peguy.
5. Leo Foxe Daniel, a person of mixed parentage, who became a Fenian and joined in the 1867 rising.
6. *A Fretful Midge* by Terence de Vere White.
7. William Carleton.
8. Canon Skerritt and Dermot O'Flingsley.
9. Samuel Beckett.
10. Lady Gregory whom he met in the office of the Abbey Theatre.
11. ' "I", said the commentator, "I killed James Joyce for my graduation." '
12. Belcher and 'Awkins.

Chapter 8

1. Sir William Butler, author of *Red Cloud, The Wild North Land* etc.
2. *The Big Chapel* by Thomas Kilroy.
3. The 1916 leader, Thomas MacDonagh.
4. At a fair in Kinvara, Co. Galway.
5. Because, "Eternally they look north towards Armagh."
6. Oliver Goldsmith.
7. Edmund Burke.
8. Louis MacNeice in "Bagpipe Music".
9. The Grey Woman of Dun Gortin and the Thin Woman of Inis Magrath.
10. Estragon, Vladimir, Lucky and Pozzo.
11. George Moore.
12. And I had a prayer like a white rose pinned
    On the Virgin Mary's blouse.

Chapter 9

1. James Stephens.
2. From Sean O'Casey who called him "English literature's performing flea."
3. J. P. Donleavy in *The Ginger Man*.
4. A Protestant on a horse.
5. He was a shoemaker.
6. Margaret Mary or Margo.
7. *Juno and the Paycock*.
8. For Mr Godot, minding his goats.
9. It was a collection of fairy stories for children.
10. George A. Birmingham.
11. Wilfred Owen.
12. Nahum Tate.

Chapter 10

1. *The Shadow of the Glen.*
2. Jonathan Swift.
3. James Clarence Mangan.
4. Thady Quirk.
5. James Joyce.
6. *The Midnight Court,* by Brian Merriman.
7. *King Goshawk and the Birds* by Eimar O'Duffy.
8. Because:
    I lost my watch in Doneraile
    My Dublin watch, my chain and seal,
    Pilfered at once in Doneraile.
9. Amanda McKittrick Ros.
10. The seagull.
11. "The girl I left behind me."
12. *More Pricks than Kicks* by Samuel Beckett.

Chapter 11

1. *My New Curate* by Canon Sheehan.

2. He wrote a 692 page book entitled *P'tit Bonhomme,* a novel purporting to give a complete picture of life in Ireland about 1875.

3. Charles Kickham fell in love with her, but though she admired him greatly, her admiration never ripened into love.

4. Daniel Corkery.

5. *An Only Child* by Frank O'Connor.

6. James Clarence Mangan and his poem "My Dark Rosaleen."

7. Standish O'Grady.

8. His personal reminiscences of the years leading up to the signing of the Anglo-Irish Treaty.

9. Mícheál Ó Guithín, poet son of Peig Sayers in a foreword to her autobiography. The original was, of course, written in Irish.

10. Rev William Lannigan.

11. His only mission hitherto had been in Manchester at St Chad's.

12. Peter Cheyney.

Chapter 12

1. Peig Sayers.
2. George Russell (AE)
3. The river Nore.
4. *Stand and Give Challenge, Candle for the Proud* and *Men Withering.*
5. The Gaelic poet, Donnchada Ruadh Mac Con Mara.
6. Red Hugh O'Donnell.
7. James Joyce.
8. Amanda McKittrick Ros. The titles of the novels are *Irene Iddesleigh, Delina Delaney* and *Helen Huddleson.*
9. *Children of the Dead End.*
10. The 1916 Rebellion and the War of Independence.
11. Joseph Sheridan Le Fanu, and Lord Dunsany.
12. *At Swim-Two-Birds* by Flann O'Brien.

Chapter 13

1. *The Islandman* by Tomás Ó Criomhthain, translated by Robin Flower.

2. *The Great Hunger* by Patrick Kavanagh.

3. Myles na gCopaleen is the name of a character in Gerald Griffin's *The Collegians*.

4. Percy Bysshe Shelley.

5. Thomas Carlyle in his *Reminiscences*.

6. Goldsmith himself! In a humorous letter to Robert Braynton of Ballymahon.

7. *Never No More* by Maura Laverty.

8. The nephew was Daniel O'Connell. The extract is from a letter from Maurice (Old Hunting Cap) O'Connell to Daniel's father.

9.   A gentle peasant girl
   With mild eyes like the dawn.

10. "The Irish Peasant Girl" by Charles J. Kickham.

11. Because it concerns the interwoven fortunes of three families: the Larkins, Catholic farmers; the MacLeods, Protestant shipyard workers; and an Anglo-Irish landed gentry family, the Hubbles.

12. Dag Hammarskjold of the United Nations and the African leader, Patrice Lumumba.

Chapter 14

1. Inspector French.

2. "The Rose of Tralee".

3. *Reflections on the Revolution in France* by Edmund Burke, published in 1790.

4. He was born in 1787 at Elm Hall, Tipperary.

5. Richard Cantillon (1680-1734). Usually called De Cantillon of Ballyheigue.

6. *An Seabhac* (The Hawk). *Jimín Mháire Thaidhg* and *An Baile Seo 'gainne.*

7. Dr M. P. O'Connor. The title of the novel: *Dreamer Awake.*

8. Esther Mary.

9. *Fairy Legends and Traditions of the South of Ireland* by Thomas Crofton Croker.

10. "Lines addressed to a Seagull, Seen off the Cliffs of Moher in the County of Clare."

11. They were leaping over bonfires in the garden of their convent, practising a custom derived from a fertility ritual.

12. A magazine, principally of Greek and Latin composition by Trinity College men. It began publication in 1874 under the editorship of Professor R. Yelverton Tyrell.

Chapter 15

1. *Children of the Rainbow* by Brian MacMahon.
2. *The Life of Riley* by Anthony Cronin.
3. *Confessions of a Young Man* by George Moore.
4. *Delina Delaney* by Amanda McKittrick Ros.
5. *Black List, Section H.* by Francis Stuart.
6. *Land* by Liam O'Flaherty.
7. *The Charwoman's Daughter* by James Stephens.
8. *The Key Above the Door* by Maurice Walsh.
9. *That Lady* by Kate O'Brien.
10. *The Saint and Mary Kate* by Frank O'Connor.
11. *Candle for the Proud* by Francis MacManus.
12. *Call for a Miracle* by Benedict Kiely.

11

987

DISCO

Chapter 16

1. Francis Joseph McPhilips.
2. Gypo Nolan.
3. James Joyce.
4. Francis Stuart.
5. The fairies.
6. "Lament for the Death of Thomas Davis."
7. Daniel O'Connell.
8. Gerald Griffin and Rev Francis Mahony, "Father Prout".
9. "The Irish Emigrant."
10. Seamus Heaney.
11. Timothy Buckley.
12. *My Cousin Justin.*

Chapter 17

1. W.B. Yeats in answer to a Mr O'Connor who asked him: "How are you?"
2. George Bernard Shaw.
3. Conor Cruise O'Brien.
4. James Joyce.
5. J.P. Donleavy.
6. Michael Collins on signing the Anglo-Irish Treaty in London, 1921.
7. Samuel Beckett.
8. Edmund Burke.
9. Oliver Goldsmith.
10. Oscar Wilde.
11. Jonathan Swift.
12. Richard Brinsley Sheridan.

Chapter 18

1. "Going Into Exile" by Liam O'Flaherty.
2. "Lovers of the Lake" by Sean O'Faolain.
3. "The Awakening" by Daniel Corkery.
4. "The Dead" by James Joyce.
5. "Cords" by Edna O'Brien.
6. "The Confirmation Suit" by Brendan Behan.
7. "A Choice of Butchers" by William Trevor.
8. "A Rhinoceros, Some Ladies, and a Horse" by James Stephens.
9. "Bomb Box" by John McGahern.
10. "Lilacs" by Mary Lavin.
11. "My Oedipus Complex" by Frank O'Connor.
12. "Unholy Living and Half Dying" by Sean O'Faolain.

Chapter 19

1. Major Sinclair Yeates.
2. They were second cousins.
3. The Dublin Verse-Speaking Society.
4. *The Honey Spike* by Bryan MacMahon.
5. *Seek the Fair Land*.
6. *Philadelphia, Here I Come!*
7. The Irish Labour Movement in the years before World War I.
8. *The MacDermots of Ballycronan*.
9. It is a fantasy set in an island off the coast of Kerry, the last place in the world to celebrate a Latin Mass.
10. Brendan Behan.
11. The Godkin family. The novel is a first-person narrative of Gabriel Godkin telling the story of his family.
12. Both of these phrases are mystical names for Ireland.

Chapter 20

1. Terence Casey.
2. Rody the Rover is the title of one of William Carleton's novels.
3. Each of them has written a life of Michael Collins.
4. Buck Mulligan was Oliver St John Gogarty and Haines was R.S. Chenevix Trench, an Englishman.
5. *Casadh an tSúgáin.*
6. Thomas Moore.
7. Edward Martyn.
8. George Fitzmaurice.
9. *Spreading the News* by Lady Gregory.
10. *The Green Fool* by Patrick Kavanagh. The sentence to which he objected reads: "I mistook Gogarty's white-robed maid for his wife – or his mistress. I expected every poet to have a spare wife."
11. Professor Denis O'Donoghue.
12. The Gate Theatre.

Anthony Cronin

HERITAGE NOW

Irish Literature in the English Language

"Anthony Cronin's reading is wide, his insights astonishing, his whole book suggests that we may well be ready for a unitarian approach to the literature of Ireland in English." –
Anthony Burgess

"This is a good book to have around. It's at once warm and intelligent in its approach. It has an extremely sensitive feel for the essential qualities of the Irish voice as expressed in literature ... The verve of the discussion, the vivid connections established, open the topics freshly to us." –
Tom McIntyre

"After years of persistent attempts to open up the closed shop of so-called Anglo-Irish literature, Anthony Cronin has flushed it out with an explosive critical device called *Heritage Now*." –
Francis Stuart

A SELECTION OF POPULAR READING FROM BRANDON

The Life of Riley by Anthony Cronin
"I have laughed more at *The Life of Riley* than at any other book I have ever read." — *The Irish Times*

Night in Tunisia by Neil Jordan
The most notable Irish short story collection of recent years; joint winner of the *Guardian* Fiction Prize.

Children of the Dead End, Glenmornan, Lanty Hanlon, Moleskin Joe and *The Rat-Pit* by Patrick MacGill
Five novels by the immensely popular Donegal writer.

Bornholm Night-Ferry by Aidan Higgins
"A marvellous, moving and fierce piece of work that does full justice to Aidan Higgins' talents and concerns, and cries out to be read and savoured." — *Image*

Boy With an Injured Eye by Ronan Sheehan
"Left me speechless with admiration." — *Evening Herald*

Baulox by Tony Cafferky
"Tony Cafferky has constructed with great skill and flair a brave new world of the late 20th century." — *In Dublin*

Grounds by Pauline Hall
"Moderation, clarity and a rhythmic sense of life are hallmarks of this excellent novel." — *Sunday Independent*

Twist and Shout, A Novel by Philip Davison
"Very alive and very funny." — *In Dublin*

Banished Misfortune by Dermot Healy
"A unique talent." — *Sunday Press*
"A writer who matters." — *Daily Telegraph*

Brandon Book Publishers Ltd, Dingle, Co. Kerry